Shimmer & Shine Annual 2019
A CENTUM BOOK 978-1-912564-54-5
Published in Great Britain by Centum Books Ltd.
This edition published 2018.
1 3 5 7 9 10 8 6 4 2

Centum Books Ltd, 20 Devon Square, Newton Abbot, Devon, TQ12 2HR, UK

books@centumbooksltd.co.uk

CENTUM BOOKS Limited Reg. No. 07641486

A CIP catalogue record for this book is available from the British Library.

Printed in Italy

SHIMMER & Shine

ANNUAL 2019

This book belongs to

....

Boom Zahramay!

Welcome to Zahramay Falls! Can you unscramble the letters to reveal each character's name?

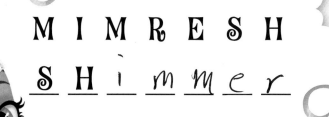

MIMRESH

Shimmer

TEZA

Zeta

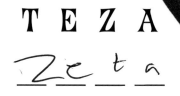

HISEN

Shine

MIRASA

Samira

LALAY

Layla

KZA

Zak
Kaz

HEAL

Leah

AZG

Zag

Find the answers on page 76

7

Zahra Zlam

Can you spot five differences between the two pictures below of Shimmer and Shine?

Tala and Nahal go everywhere with Shimmer and Shine and love riding on their flying carpet.

Tick a star when you spot a difference. →

Too easy? Now try and spot seven differences between these two pictures too.

Find the answers on page 76

Wild Carpet Chase

Zac has wished up a cool magic carpet but Zeta has zoomed off on it. Can you find a way through the clouds to help Zac get it back?

START

10

FINISH

Zeta dreams of being the most powerful person in Zahramay Falls.

Find the answers on page 76

Sweet Shimmer

Shimmer is bursting with energy and loves to go on magical adventures in Zahramay Falls.

Shimmer's pet Tala is always by her side, or climbing on her head!

Shimmer loves to dance. Can you spot 5 ballet shoes hidden on the page? When you do, colour them in.

Make this picture of Shimmer sparkle with your best colours.

Shimmer's jewels are sparkly and green.

She always looks on the bright side and hopes for the best.

Find the answers on page 76

13

Cleanie Genie

Shimmer and Shine are using the pristine gem to help clean their genie palace but Zeta wants it for herself!

1   2   3

Which sparkly dust trail leads to the pristine gem? Which one ends at a broom?

Now can you work out which pieces go where to put the broken potion bottle back together?

Find the answers on page 76

sparkly shine

Bold and courageous, Shine is always up for lots of fun and some genie magic!

Shine loves animals, especially her cute cub Nahal.

Shine always has lots of wise words, which she often makes up on the spot. Tick the saying that she is most likely to say.

Zip zow, open now!

That's not what I wished for!

That's because I just made it up!

Join the dots and add some sparkly colours to finish this picture of Shine.

Shine is very confident but if she makes mistakes she keeps trying to get things right.

Yummy Wishes

Help Shimmer and Shine make a delicious cake for Leah by putting a tick next to the items you need for baking and a cross next to the ones you don't.

mixer

kettle

sugar

ball

oven

skateboard

egg

shimmer loves pink icing as it's her favourite colour.

flour

milk

bellows

mixing bowl

Find the answers on page 76

19

Kind Leah

Leah is very caring and does whatever it takes to make her friends happy.

Leah summons Shimmer and Shine with her genie bottle necklace.

She loves to dress up for lots of fun adventures with her friends.

Leah always thinks things through before making decisions.

Trace over the lines to finish off this magical picture of Leah making a wish!

Leah is thrilled to have genie friends. How many wishes does she get to make a day?

1   2   3

Find the answers on page 76

sparkly shopping

The girls are shopping together and trying on some fun outfits. Draw a line to match the outfit they should choose for the activities below.

trick or treating

skateboarding

fairy party

beach

masked ball

ballet lesson

sleepover party

deep-sea swimming

1

2

3

4

5

6

7

8

Now choose another fun activity for the girls to try and draw a sparkly outfit for them to wear in the space below.

⭐ horse riding ✓

⭐ cooking

⭐ football

⭐ tap dancing

⭐ gymnastics

⭐ gardening

Find the answers on page 76

Cute Cat

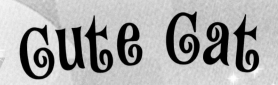

Feisty Nahal loves cuddles and getting up to mischief.

Nahal can be quite cautious and scares easily.

Nahal loves to pounce on whatever takes her fancy and enjoys lots of tummy tickles.

Add some colour to Nahal's fluffy fur.

Monkey Mischief

Tala is a mischief-making little gibbon and loves going on magical adventures.

Join the dots to finish this cheeky monkey!

Tala's curious nature often lands her in trouble.

Tala loves to play games with her friends, especially hide and seek!

Backyard Ballet

Read the story about Leah's dancing adventure. When you see a character say their name.

Leah

Shine

Zac

Shimmer

 and Zac were twirling and leaping around Leah's living room, practising to put on their own ballet.

 left to go home and Leah wished she could dance like the real Swan Queen in the ballet Swan Lake.

'Boom, Zahramay! First wish of the day!' chanted , suddenly appearing with her twin sister Shimmer.

Leah found herself dressed as the Swan Queen from the ballet – but with six loud swans as royal subjects!

'Oh dear,' Leah said. 'I was hoping to spin like the ballerina Swan Queen, not be the actual queen of six swans.'

 frowned. 'Oopsie! It sounds like I made a mistake.'

Leah had to get the swans outside before they destroyed the whole house. 'I wish the swans would follow me!' she cried.

Shimmer jangled her magic bracelets.

'Boom, Zahramay! Second wish of the day!'

The swans followed into the backyard but Leah still hadn't practised any ballet. She made her final wish. 'I wish to be a ballerina in *Swan Lake*!'

Suddenly her back garden was transformed into a giant lake!

'This is beautiful, but I wanted to dance like the ballerina from *Swan Lake,*

not have an actual lake,' smiled.

'Sorry, Leah. I didn't mean to make such a big mistake,' said .

Leah hugged Shine. 'It's okay. No mistake is too big to fix. Even one

as big as a lake! Let's get back to dry land so we can practise spinning!'

Suddenly, she slipped and fell, then bounced off a lily pad and did a perfect

ballerina spin.

'WOW! That was amazing!' said .

Leah kept bouncing and spinning from pad to pad. The swans did the same.

'If I keep practising,' she said, 'maybe I'll finally spin like the Swan Queen!'

Later in the day, came back to see Leah.

'Whoa!' he shouted to Leah. 'There's a lake and swans in your back garden!'

'Wanna dance?' Leah asked and the two friends

had lots of fun spinning and leaping around together.

Afterwards, found and .

'We fixed our mistakes and the day turned

out great!' Leah said and hugged her genie

friends. Then Leah and Zac put

on a magical performance!

Sassy Sorceress

Zeta loves to zoom around Zahramay Falls on her speedy scooter with her loyal sidekick, Nazboo.

After failing genie school, Zeta had to settle for sorceress status instead. She wants to be more powerful than anyone else in Zahramay Falls and loves making potions.

Can you spot 5 potion bottles on the page? When you do, colour them in.

Join the dots to finish this picture of Zeta, then colour her in.

Selfish and scheming Zeta cheats and steals to get her hands on as many Genie Gems as she can. She is always up to no good.

Find the answers on page 76

Dream Doll's House

Shimmer and Shine have shrunk so they can play with Leah in her doll's house.

Can you spot them and the items below inside?

When Leah's doll's house gets broken, Shimmer and Shine help her build a new one!

Find the answers on page 76

Flower Power

Colour in all the flowers to make Leah's wish for a pretty garden come true.

Colour in the biggest flower red.

Can you spot a flower with just three petals?

Colour in the smallest flower blue.

Find the answers on page 76

Oh My Genie

Help Shimmer and Shine at genie school by cracking the codes to reveal the answers.

1 Circle every third letter to reveal what Princess Samira is teaching the genies in training.

T R Ⓢ U V Ⓟ D L Ⓔ T M Ⓛ S O Ⓛ G H Ⓢ

S P e L L S

2 Now cross out every letter that appears three times to discover what lesson is next.

G P Ⓛ R Q Q
B G Ⓡ T R
I Q Q Ⓑ L N
Ⓛ S G Q B

L O I I B L V

3 Finally turn each letter below into the next letter in the alphabet to reveal what Princess Samira rewards good pupils with.

F D L R

g e m s

Find the answers on page 77

Genie Craft

Follow the simple steps below and use the template opposite to create your own genie-tastic fortune teller.

Ask a grown-up to help you with the tricky bits.

1 Cut out the template on page 35, then fold each corner to the opposite corner. Then open up again to create creases in your paper.

The four characters should now be showing.

2 Fold all corners to the centre of the square.

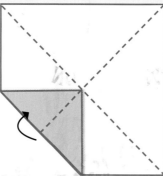

It should now look like this.

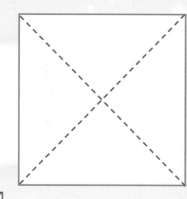

3 Next, turn your template over so the folds are face down and fold each corner in to the centre.

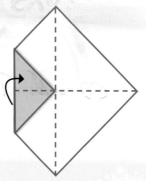

Now you should see the numbers.

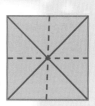

4 Next, fold your template in half vertically and then again horizontally.

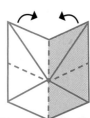 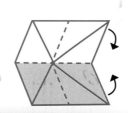

5 Insert your fingers and thumbs underneath the flaps you have created.

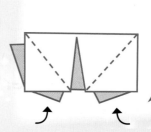 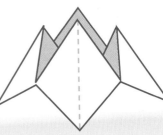

How to play

1 Ask a question that has a yes or no answer and pick a character.

2 Open the fortune teller in alternating directions, one time each for every letter of the character's name.

3 Then pick a number and open the fortune teller this many times, in alternating directions.

4 Pick another number then lift that flap to reveal the answer to your question.

If you prefer, you could cut along the dotted line and have this page as a poster instead.

Be Jewelled

Help Zeta to collect Genie Gems by counting up how many there are on the page.

Find the answers on page 77

Write your answer here.

I counted

20

gems.

Best Buddies

Quirky but sweet, Zac is Leah's best friend and loves going on magical adventures.

Zac loves exploring Zahramay Falls!

Join the dots and add some colour to this giggling Zac.

Zac is never shocked by all the strange things that happen to him and his genie friends.

38

Clever Genie

Kaz knows everything there is to know about Zahramay Falls, making him the perfect genie guide for Zac when he visits.

Make Kaz sparkle with your best colours.

Kaz had never met a non-magical person before Zac.

Kaz often worries about things and likes to follow the rules.

Rainbow Hair

The Hair Genie has turned Shimmer and Shine's hair all the colours of the rainbow. Follow the colour key to finish off their hairstyles then colour the rest of them in too.

What colour hair do you have?

COLOUR CODE

1 = red
2 = green
3 = blue
4 = yellow
5 = pink
6 = orange
7 = purple

Shine is the older genie twin by just two minutes!

Royal Ruler

Kind and caring Princess Samira is in charge of all magic in Zahramay Falls.

Tick true or false to the statements below:

1

Princess Samira is the most powerful genie in Zahramay Falls.

True ✓ False

2

She lives in a palace in Zahramay Falls.

True ✓ False

3

Her pet peacock is called Raymond.

True ✓ False

Find the answers on page 77

As mentor to all genies in training, she likes to award Genie Gems to those who deserve them.

Trace over the lines to finish this picture of Princess Samira, then colour her and the Genie Gems in.

Rainbow Zahramay

Help Shimmer and Shine find their way through the maze to the colourful rainbow waterfall.

START

FINISH

Which path should they take to reach Imma?

1

2

3

Imma is a magical genie who controls the rainbow waterfall.

Find the answers on page 77

45

Friends Forever

Can you fit all of the sparkly, magical friends' names into the word grid opposite?

KAZ

TALA

SHINE ✓

PARISA

ZAC

Don't forget to colour in all the magical friends with your best colours.

SHIMMER

LEAH

NAHAL

Find the answers on page 77

47

Wish Upon A Sleepover

Colour in the pictures to finish off this genie adventure.

Leah had invited Shimmer and Shine to their first sleepover party. 'There's pizza, music and dancing. And we get to sleep in a pillow fort!' said Leah and showed the genies how to make a fort – but they needed more pillows.

'For my first wish,' Leah said, 'I wish for more pillows!'

'Boom, Zahramay! First wish of the day!' chanted Shine.

Suddenly, pillows were everywhere, filling the room up to the ceiling! Leah looked at the piles of pillows.

'I was thinking six not a whole roomful.'

Shine smiled bashfully. 'My mistake.'

After playing with the pillows, Leah tried to put on some songs, but her music player was broken.

'For my second wish, I wish we could play music!' said Leah.

Shimmer spun her bracelets. 'Boom, Zahramay! Second wish of the day!'

In a puff of smoke the girls found themselves surrounded by instruments!

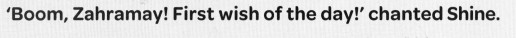

'I didn't mean to wish for instruments. I just wanted my music player to work. Maybe we can make our own music for the dance party!' said Leah.

Shine sprinkled some dust over the instruments and they began to play.

'This is a blast!' Leah said. 'I wish the dancing would never stop!'

Shine clapped her hands. 'Boom, Zahramay! Third wish of the day!'

Leah laughed as they all danced around, but the girls eventually grew tired.

'We need to stop dancing, but there are no wishes left!' said Leah.

'Even my ears are tired,' Shine said, holding a pillow over each ear, which drowned out the music.

'Shine, you've stopped dancing!' exclaimed Leah. With a magical wave, Shimmer collapsed the pillow fort onto the instruments. The music stopped and so did the dancing!

Leah hugged her friends. 'We fixed our mistakes, and the night turned out great!'

Shine yawned. 'Now it's time to get some sleep at this sleepover party!'

Roya

This beautiful bird is proud to be pet peacock to Princess Samira.

Roya loves to practise walking gracefully.

Once a year Roya sheds a single feather that can fix a broken object.

Fluff up Roya's feathers and copy her colours to finish the picture above.

50

Nazboo

Zeta's loyal sidekick always does his best to please his bossy owner, but he often gets distracted by the thought of what food he'd like to eat!

Nazboo always makes his point with snorts and snuffles.

Nazboo loves having his tummy tickled - a lot!

Now copy Nazboo's colours to finish his picture too.

51

powerful potions

Help Zeta finish off her potions by colouring in all the bottles.

Colour in the biggest bottle pink and the smallest bottle green.

Zip Zow

Nazboo is on a mission to find Zeta the following things in the market place.

Can you help him find:

1 magic carpet

2 skateboards

3 potion bottles

4 gems

5 genie lamps

Find the answers on page 77

Mermaid Mayhem

Leah has wished the girls can join Nila on a mermaid adventure – help her wish come true by working out which pieces go where to complete their mermaid tails.

1

2

3

A

B

C

who else can you spot swimming with a fishy tail?

6

5

4

D

E

F

pet Games

Oopsie! All the pets have multiplied. Can you spot the odd one out in each row?

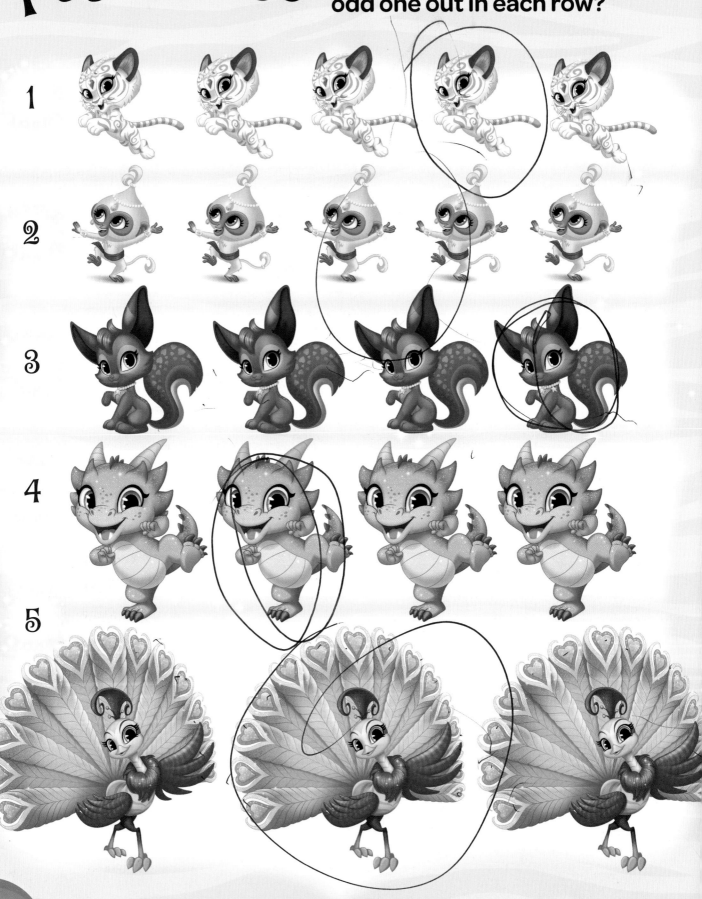

Now find 5 differences between these pictures of Zain. Tick them off when you spot them.

Zain is Kaz's pet and the biggest in Zahramay Falls.

Find the answers on page 77

57

Going Dotty

Join the dots then colour in the picture of Shimmer, Shine and Leah with Dotty the elephant.

Shimmer, Shine and Leah often make mistakes on their adventures but they never give up till they get things right.

pretty pet

Leah's fun fox Parisa loves going on magical adventures.

Parisa also enjoys making mischief with Nahal and Tala.

You'll need a purple pen to finish off this picture of Leah's cute pet.

Circle every other letter to reveal Parisa's special skill.

T C B A R M D O L U
T F R L C A R G T E

C

Find the answers on page 77

Turn the page for a fun game using this cut-out of Nahal.

Which magical pet is your favourite?

Animal Magic

Follow the simple steps below and use the templates of Nahal and Tala to create a fun game.

1   Cut along the dotted lines to cut out Nahal, Tala and their tails.

2   Place the magical pets' bodies onto a flat surface (like a table).

3   Take it in turns with a family member or friend to take each pet's tail, close your eyes and place each tail where you think it should go.

4   Open your eyes and see how close you got to the right spot, then let the other player have a turn. The one who gets closest, wins.

Ask a grown-up to help you with the tricky bits.

Try to make them like this.

Tala loves green jewels, just like her owner Shimmer.

If you had a pet monkey, what would you call it?

Winged Wonder

Kaz's unique pet Zain loves to zoom around Zahramay Falls.

This fun-loving Ziffilon has the tail of a lion but a giant bird beak.

Zain loves playing games with the other pets.

Colour in Zain's feathers to complete his picture.

Be Genie-rific

Can you find all these characters and places in the wordsearch opposite? Tick them off when you spot them.

- ☆ BOOM ZAHRAMAY
- ☆ GEMS
- ☆ GENIE
- ☆ LEAH
- ☆ MAGIC
- ☆ RAINBOW
- ☆ SHIMMER
- ☆ SHINE
- ☆ SPARKLE
- ☆ WATERFALL
- ~~ZETA~~

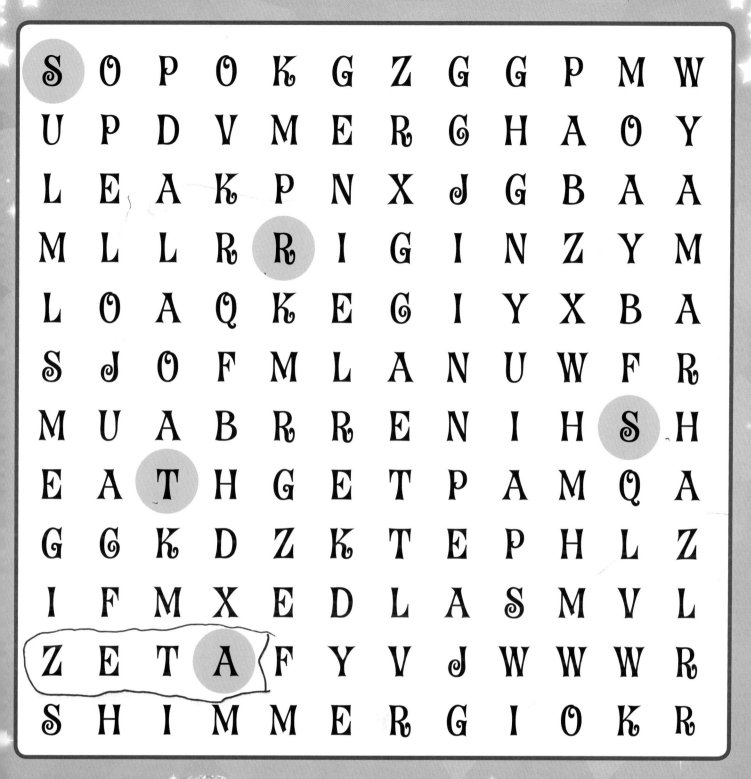

S	S	O	P	O	K	G	Z	G	G	P	M	W
U	P	D	V	M	E	R	G	H	A	O	Y	
L	E	A	K	P	N	X	J	G	B	A	A	
M	L	L	R	R	I	G	I	N	Z	Y	M	
L	O	A	Q	K	E	G	I	Y	X	B	A	
S	J	O	F	M	L	A	N	U	W	F	R	
M	U	A	B	R	R	E	N	I	H	S	H	
E	A	T	H	G	E	T	P	A	M	Q	A	
G	G	K	D	Z	K	T	E	P	H	L	Z	
I	F	M	X	E	D	L	A	S	M	V	L	
Z	E	T	A	F	Y	V	J	W	W	W	R	
S	H	I	M	M	E	R	G	I	O	K	R	

Don't forget to look forwards, backwards and diagonally too!

Write the letters in pink circles below to reveal a sparkly word.

S t a r s

Find the answers on page 77

67

Treasure Twins

Colour in the pictures and draw some of your own to help Leah's wish for a magical seaside adventure come true.

Leah was at the beach,

collecting sea shells to make

a necklace when a huge wave

came and washed them all away.

Colour in this picture of Leah in her swimming costume.

Join the dots to finish this picture of Shimmer and Shine.

Leah wished Shimmer and

Shine could help her find

some more treasures and

BOOM ZAHRAMAY – her

magical genies appeared.

Doodle in some details on this treasure map.

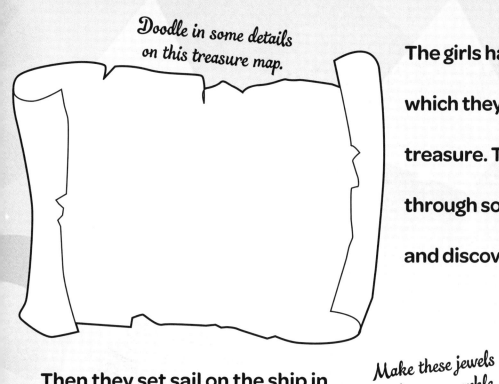

The girls had a treasure map which they used to hunt for treasure. They wandered through some tunnels in the rock and discovered a pirate ship.

Then they set sail on the ship in search of treasures and finally discovered a treasure chest filled with sparkly gems.

Make these jewels and gems sparkle with your brightest colours.

Leah used the gems to make her friends sparkly necklaces to thank them for such a fun adventure.

I Wish... I Wish...

Look at the pictures then use the word bank below to describe what Leah has wished for.

1

....

....

....

2

....

....

....

ride	sleigh	boat	skateboard	Santa	with
and	doll	a	in	tail	cow
friend	Zac	adventure	Shine	fun
on	Leah	magical	Shimmer	mermaid

3

4

....
....
....

5

6

....
....
....

Animal Magic

The six pictures opposite may look the same as the one below, but there's something different in each one. Can you spot what?

Find the answers on page 77

1

2

3

4

5

6

Genie Quiz

Put your genie know-how to the test and prove what a genie-us you are with this fun quiz.

Tick true or false to the statements below:

1 Zeta flies around on a broomstick.

True   False ✓

2 Shine's pet is called Parisa.

True   False ✓

3 Tala is a tiger.

True   False ✓

4 Zac's genie is called Kaz.

True ✓   False

5 The waterfall genie is called Imma.

True ✓   False

6 Zeta failed genie school.

True ✓   False

7 Shimmer's favourite colour is pink.

True ✓   False

8 Princess Samira's pet is a peacock called Roya.

True ✓   False

9 Leah gets to make 10 wishes a day.

True   False ✓

10 Zain is the smallest pet in Zahramay Falls.

True   False ✓

Find the answers on page 77

Dress-up Time

Follow the simple steps below to have lots of fun dressing up your Shimmer and Shine cut-out characters.

1. Remove the pages with your characters, outfits, props and stands from the back of the book.

2. Stick these pages to some thin card using glue. You could recycle an old cereal or shoe box.

3. Carefully cut along the dotted lines to cut out each character, outfit, prop and stand.

4. Slot the stands into your character cut-outs, so they stand up.

5. Fold the tabs on the outfits over, then slot them into the slits on Shimmer and Shine.

6. Have lots of fun playing with all your magical cut-out play pieces.

Mix and match your outfits to make Shine sparkle!

Ask a grown-up to help you with the tricky bits.

Think of a fun adventure for Shimmer and Shine for each outfit.

Answers

Pages 6-7
SHIMMER, ZETA, SHINE, SAMIRA, LAYLA, KAZ, LEAH, ZAC

Pages 8 -9

Pages 10-11

Pages 12-13

Page 14
Trail 3 leads to the gem, trail 1 to the broom.

Page 15
1-C, 2-G, 3-E, 4-F, 5-D, 6-A, 7-B

Page 16
That's because I just made it up!

Page 18-19
milk, flour, sugar, mixer, egg, oven, mixing bowl

Page 21
Leah has three wishes a day

Page 22
trick or treating - 3, skateboarding - 5, fairy party - 4, beach - 2, masked ball - 7, ballet lesson - 1, sleepover party - 8, deep-sea swimming - 6

Pages 28-29

Pages 30-31

Page 32

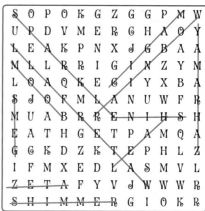
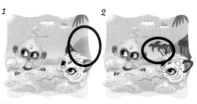

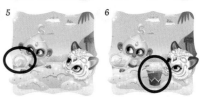

© Viacom

© Viacom

© Viacom

© Viacom

© Viacom

© Viacom

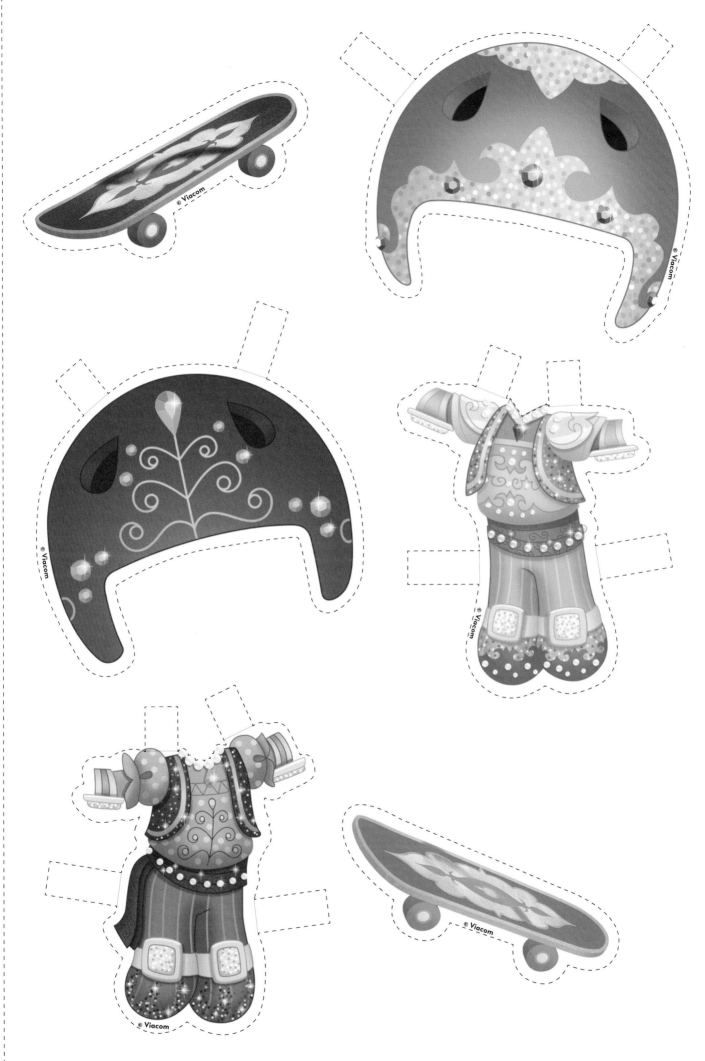